Bob's BROKEN BONE

My FRACTURE Surgery

Written & Illustrated by

Dr. Abraham Thomas

I can touch the skies !!

Oops! I missed it…

I heard a crack.
It is hurting heaps...

My arm is getting quiet sore and swollen too!
I ran to mum and she said I may have
broken a bone…

We went to the Emergency Rooms and the Doc there had a good look at my arm. He took a special picture called X RAY to look closer at my bones.

Doc said that I smashed a bone in my arm and the broken bones are bend at an odd angle . I will need a SURGERY to fix it.

Mann!! I thought I will get away
with a plaster cast like last time.

I am really scared now.

Does that mean that they will chop
my arm off !

They asked me to stop eating and
drinking from now on.

Later they gave me a special
gown to wear.

They slipped a plastic needle into my arm
called CANNULA.

They started to give me some watery stuff
called IV FLUIDS through it .

They were planning to give me medicines
through that plastic needle too….

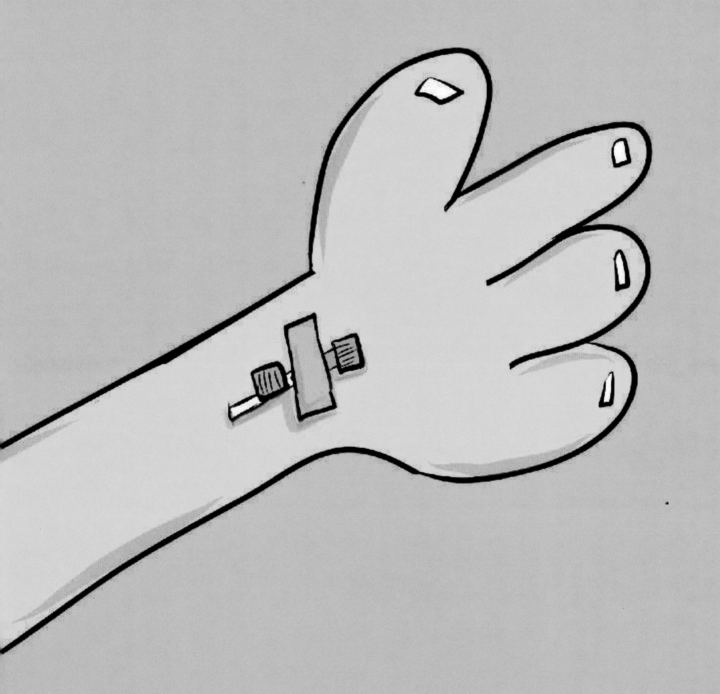

They wheeled me into a fancy room with lots of giant lights hanging from the ceiling. It was called the OPERATING THEATRE.

This is where they will do my surgery.

It had a lot of cool gadgets too to monitor me when they were operating on
my broken bone.

I had to say goodbye to mum for some time.

They slipped a mask on to my face
and gave me a special gas.

They gave me some stuff through my
cannula too.

Soon I slipped into a deep sleep.

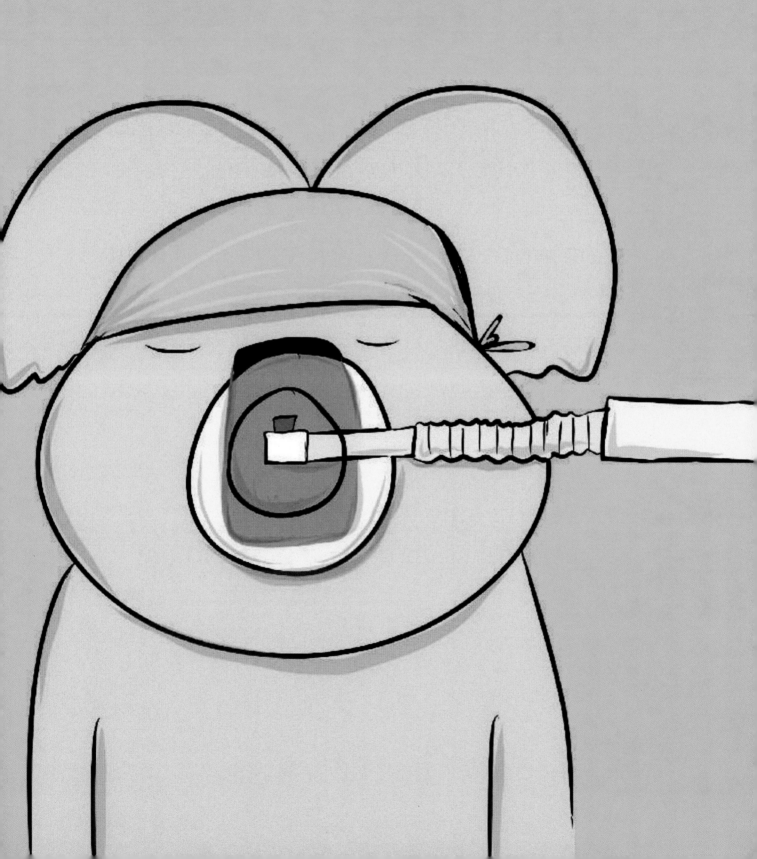

I saw a dream that Doc put a plate and a couple of screws to hold all the broken pieces of bone together.

I soon woke up in a quiet place called the **RECOVERY ROOM**.

I was relieved to see mum smiling and holding my hand.

I looked and saw that my broken arm is still there but covered in a plaster cast.

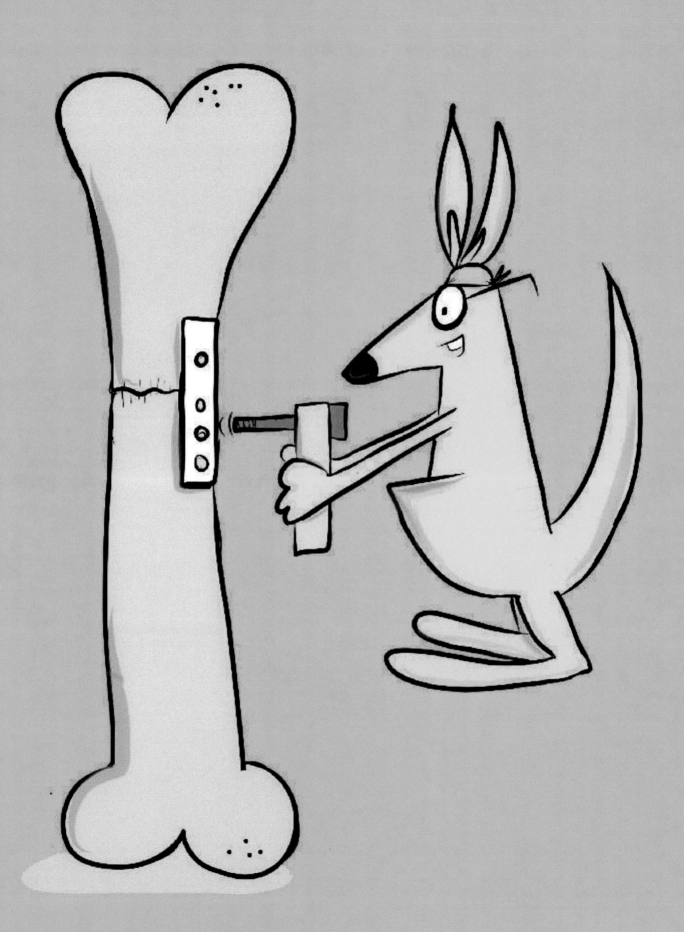

They took another X ray and Doc was happy that my broken bone were all in place. He let me go home after taking my cannula out.

My friends got a chance to write
over my plaster cast.
My bestie drew a dinosaur on it.....

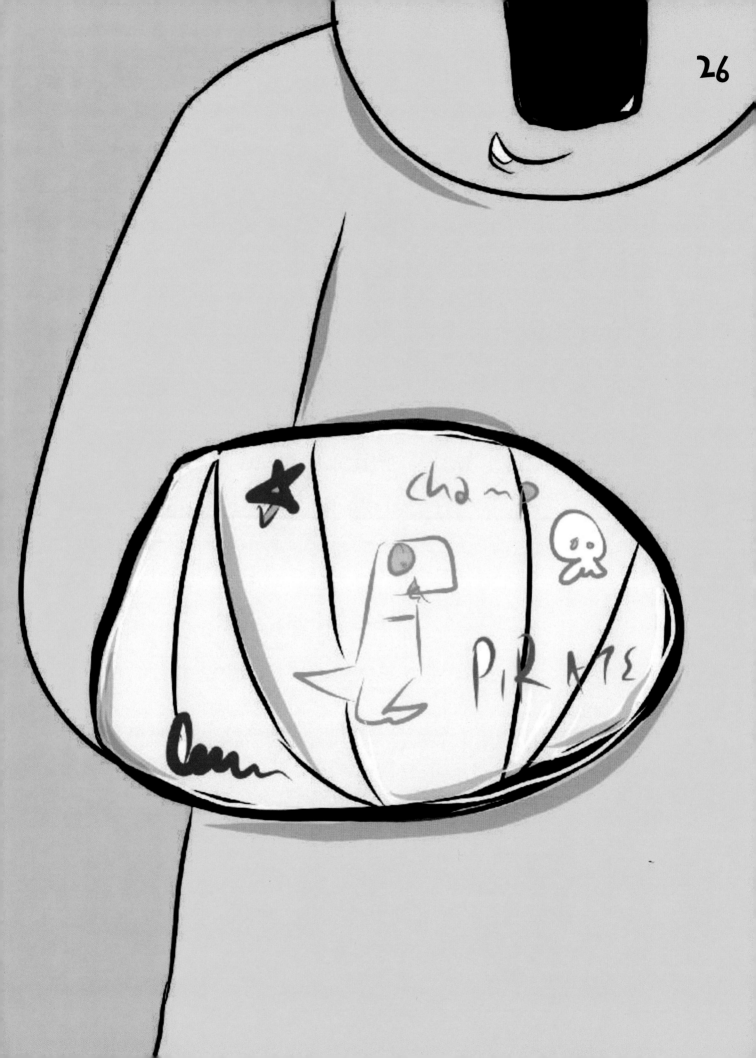

After a few weeks they took my plaster cast off. Doc said that the metal plate and screws in my bones will stay.

My broken arm is super strong now that I can do a handstand on it !!!!

TO MY WONDERFUL NEVA & AIDEN

First published by LIGHT AUSTRALIA in 2023

Design and Layout by Grafixo.

ISBN: 978-0-6457217-0-6

The illustrations of this book is created in digital media by Dr. Abraham Thomas.

Type set in Arial

Printed in Australia

A catalogue record of this book is available from the National Library of Australia